The Patient-Centred Dental Practice

The Patient-Centred Dental Practice

Philip Newsome BChD, MBA, PhD, FDS, MRD
Associate Professor
Faculty of Dentistry
The University of Hong Kong

Series Editor
Fiona Stuart-Wilson, MA(Cantab), Assoc. IPD, MIMC CMC

2001

Published by the British Dental Association
64 Wimpole Street, London W1G 8YS

ISBN 0 904588 69 6

Printed and bound by
Dennis Barber Limited, Lowestoft,
Suffolk

Foreword

Sometimes the simplest truths are the most difficult to grasp. How many times every day do we all forget to make that extra effort to understand, support, enable and motivate the people around us? All the finest management theories, structures and processes, and strategies in the world ultimately depend on the behaviour and performance of people. It is people who make things happen, or not, in whatever field of life we work.

The 'return' for good relationships, with your teams or customers, so often makes the difference. Enabling our children and our colleagues to dream and aspire, being a good listener and sensitive to those around us, creating a culture where people feel valued and are motivated to create and contribute, are all daily skills which can be continually improved upon. This book helps unlock those truths.

Richard Gregory

Managing Director Yorkshire Television;
Deputy Chair, Yorkshire Forward, the Regional Development Agency for
Yorkshire and the Humber; Chairman, Sheffield Hallam University;
Non-Executive Director of the Yorkshire and Clydesdale Banks.

Preface

Most books on practice management tend to focus on ways of making the practice more efficient and, of course, more profitable. They are, in other words, centred primarily on the needs of the dentist. This approach usually ignores the person who is ultimately the source of those profits – the patient. It is therefore the aim of this book to show that the success of every dental practice rests solely on its ability to attract and retain patients and that much more emphasis should therefore be placed on seeing things through their eyes.

Philip Newsome
Hong Kong

Contents

Why should you be concerned about patient satisfaction?

1

If we provide real satisfaction to real customers – we will be profitable.

John Young, former CEO of Hewlett Packard

These days it is almost impossible to find any practising dentists who don't also see themselves, at least to some extent, as entrepreneurs and business people. Consequently it is not too surprising that most dentists place financial success high on their list of priorities. However, despite being the ultimate business goal, profit isn't necessarily the best measure of how well a commercial enterprise is doing. Answering the question often asked by dentists, namely, 'How successful is my practice?' may not be as easy as it seems.

Businesses can, and do, use a number of diverse criteria to judge success. For example, *In Search of Excellence* (Peters and Waterman, 1982) describes several traditional measures of 'excellence' (such as profitability and growth), identifies the highest performers along these measures and then encourages other businesses to follow the behaviour and practices of these 'successful' companies. The problem, however, is that it has become clear that the subsequent performance of these so-called excellent companies has been dreadful. Of the forty-three outstanding companies chosen by Peters and Waterman, only fourteen were doing well five years later and only five after ten years. Many have disappeared altogether.

Similarly, in the UK, the business publication *Management Today* has, each year since 1995, identified the country's best, most admired, companies. Five years on from that first report, only four companies made it into the top ten in 1999, the most notable 'drop out' being Marks & Spencer with one of the most dramatic corporate declines seen in recent years.

Profitability, often expressed in terms of return on invested capital (%ROI), is probably the most commonly used measure of business success. As far as dental practice is concerned it can be defined as the average pre-tax return on invested capital after deducting fair compensation for the dentist-owner. Unfortunately, indices based on profit show a number of flaws, the most important being that they measure the *past* results of a business and not its future potential. Focussing on profitability as the primary goal invariably encourages short-term thinking and sacrifices long-term competitiveness. As the Body Shop's Anita Roddick once observed, it is like driving while all the time looking in the rear view mirror to see where you have just been.

Productivity is another performance measure commonly recommended for use by dentists. Unfortunately, practices driven by productivity usually focus solely on achieving high output levels without giving due consideration to what might be best for the patient. In addition, high productivity is often accompanied by low fee collection, leading to bad debts and poor cash flow – hardly a recipe for commercial success.

A fundamental problem of these approaches is that they ignore the customer, in our case the patient. Generally speaking, customers are free to choose from a range of products and services, including dental care, and unless what is provided satisfies the customer at least as well as that offered by the competition then profitability will quickly be eroded. If we accept that patients are the ultimate source of a practice's revenue, then efficiency in acquiring, satisfying and retaining them should be a vital factor in determining long-term financial health. Indeed, this assertion seems so manifestly obvious, that the question in the title of this chapter may seem a bit of a daft one. After all, patients are human beings and it is natural to want to provide a service that is attentive, helpful and polite. And yet, how often are we confronted in our own daily lives by what we see as being poor service? As Ted Johns (1994) writes in *Perfect Customer Care*:

> *The idea that all organisations have customers has burst only recently upon a stupefied and complacent world. Some have yet to acknowledge that the customer concept applies to them…some have embraced the notion of customer care but have done little else; some are doing their best but are rather better at talking at their customers than at listening to them. So while a few organisations lead the way, others have a lot to learn.*

So far so good. However, let's play devil's advocate for a moment and look at some situations in which satisfying patients might not, on the face of it, be so important after all. Suppose, for example, that all the practices in a particular neighbourhood simply don't seem to care too much about trying to satisfy their patients. The result is that the public gets used to an inferior level of service. Patients who need and want treatment have to go somewhere and as long as all the practices continue in this way patient satisfaction becomes irrelevant. Alternatively, a practice may be competing on price. Its charges are very low in comparison to the opposition's, patients are still coming through the door and there seems little or no reason to change. Yet another scenario is where there may effectively be no competition, no other dentists that patients can see, or at least not easily. You only have to think about the depressing level of services offered by organisations who hold such monopoly positions to realise that the words 'consumer satisfaction' hold little or no meaning. A final possibility is that you may truly be a genius with clinical skills that seem out of this world to us mere mortals. We have all heard about, maybe even worked with such autocratic superstars who are always right, and whose technical brilliance and status puts them in the position of always being able to boss staff around, pick and choose their patients, make them wait, and give them what is good for them. Indeed, for some patients it may even be reassuring to know that someone is so obviously in command and that the rest of the 'team' is being kept in order.

If you fit into any of the above descriptions you may not wish to read any further, but do so at your peril. All the above situations are transitory, hazardous and will ultimately, in all probability, lead to business failure. Let's look again at the above situations to find out why. In the first, trouble arises when (not if) somebody comes along and seeks a competitive advantage by developing a reputation for high quality service. The recent arrival in the dental marketplace of high-profile, market-driven corporate players should act as a wake up call to everyone in the profession. The commercial benefit of improved patient care, consumer care, can be seen as the battleground from which the future of the profession will emerge.

Equally, competing on price alone, as in the second example, is short term in the extreme. As will be discussed later in Chapter 3, all the evidence points to the fact that the actual cost of treatment is seen to be less of an issue for most patients than the manner in which the practice communicates information about that cost. Clearly, if all other things, ie the overall service package, are equal then lower price may well become an important issue. However, it is difficult to imagine a dental practice, whose guiding ethos is that of cutting costs, spending the time and energy necessary on researching and then implementing excellent, across the board, service quality. It is a delusion to believe that price is the sole determinant of what customers like. The world's favourite airline is far from being the cheapest.

The third example, that of holding a monopoly position, rarely lasts for ever and when competition does arrive the challenge can be virtually impossible to counter – with one's head in the sand it is extremely difficult to prepare for the changes that are required. If you do find yourself in this monopoly position, please act as though you are not. By overcoming the complacency inherent in this situation you will be in a much better position to face the competition when the inevitable happens and it does show its face.

Finally, if you really are a genius carrying out complex procedures beyond the scope of the average dentist then perhaps you can be as autocratic as you like. However, you can only afford to be a moody, bossy egomaniac as long as your talents are in demand. Eventually, patients and staff will either get fed up with your arrogance and move on, or alternatively become as awkward and demanding as you, making life far more difficult than it need be. Where's the genius in that?

Whatever the size, type and location of your practice, whatever kind of dentist you are, creating patient satisfaction and maybe even patient delight, should be a never-ending odyssey. But let's not get too carried away – many books and articles are now talking of even astounding or astonishing customers, whereas simple satisfaction is perhaps a more realistic aim. Importantly, it is an aim that can be achieved. As *Financial Times* writer Lucy Kellaway put it:

> *Lots of things delight me, from the birth of a baby to seeing the Rolling Stones in concert. But when it comes to my life as a consumer, I usually aim for satisfaction, which I get when I buy something I want at a price I can afford.*

External and internal customers

I am sure that every dentist alive remembers being told as a student something along the lines of, 'We are going to make you think like a dentist' when what we should have been told was, 'We are going to make you think like a patient'. Even this approach is somewhat lacking as it assumes that patients are our only customers. An approach more in keeping with modern management thinking is to use the term customer to apply to 'the person with whom you are dealing at the moment and whom you are trying to help', ie whether they are inside or outside the practice. Frances and Roland Bee stress the importance of this in their book *Customer Care* (1995):

> *The quality of customer care offered to internal customers is just as vital as that offered to external customers, and that in successful organisations everyone operates as though all their colleagues are cherished and important customers.*

In a typical dental practice such internal customer relationships include those between the dentist, the surgery assistant, the reception staff, the dental laboratory and so on. Each party should identify each other's needs and do their best to meet and, wherever possible, better them. If staff members are struggling to get their colleagues to meet their particular needs then nobody is focussing on meeting the requirements of the ultimate customer, the patient. For example, the dentist forgetting to tell the receptionist that he or she is going on a course the following week, or requesting that all emergencies be scheduled the same day (that the patient phones) and then complaining because the appointment book is too congested. The importance of such internal relationships in driving profit can be seen in the 'Service Profit Chain':

- Profit is closely related to…
- Customer retention – anyone who can retain customers has a competitive advantage, which is closely related to…
- Customer satisfaction which is determined largely by the customer perception of value which results from an assessment of…
- Perceived service quality which is likely to be greater in organisations characterised by…
- Employee retention – itself associated with thoughtful staff selection, effective training, compensation related in part to performance and derived from…
- Employee satisfaction which is consistently higher when…
- Internal service quality is high.

None of these factors operate in isolation and the notion that consistently high-quality service leads to sustainable profitability is now undeniable. The returns from improved service quality have been well documented and in the long run the most important single factor affecting a business's performance is the quality of its products and services compared to those of its competitors. Superior quality is the most effective way for a business to grow.

Evidence for this comes from the PIMS (Profit Impact of Marketing Strategy) database, which contains information about strategy and performance from more than 2600 businesses. It demonstrates that quality care buys businesses the following key advantages.

- Stronger customer loyalty.
- More repeat purchases.
- Less vulnerability to price.
- Ability to command high relative price.
- Lower marketing costs.

An ever increasing number of studies have begun to confirm that these findings also apply to healthcare providers and while little work has been done to replicate these findings in the sphere of dental practice, it seems reasonable to assume that such a correlation does exist (Figure 1.1).

As can be seen from this diagram, patients who are satisfied with the service they have received are likely to spread positive word of mouth as well as referring patients to the practice that has provided that good service. Such satisfied patients are also likely to continue patronising the practice and be willing to pay a price premium for the range of services provided. It is not unusual for patients to consider more complex treatment options after they have been attending the practice for some time and therefore feel more confident about their choice of practice. Dissatisfied patients tend to do exactly the opposite. At best, such patients will simply spend less and perhaps (if you are lucky) voice their complaints to the practice. At worst, they will find another dentist as well as spreading damaging negative word of mouth about the practice to their family and friends.

Last but not least, satisfied patients cause less stress for everyone in the practice. All of us, at some time or another, have had to deal with a dissatisfied patient and know the pressure such situations can bring. Complaints always seem to come at the busiest times and there is nothing more demotivating for staff than having to deal with complaints in front of other patients. Satisfied patients, on the other hand, bring job satisfaction, take up less of your time and help motivate the whole dental team.

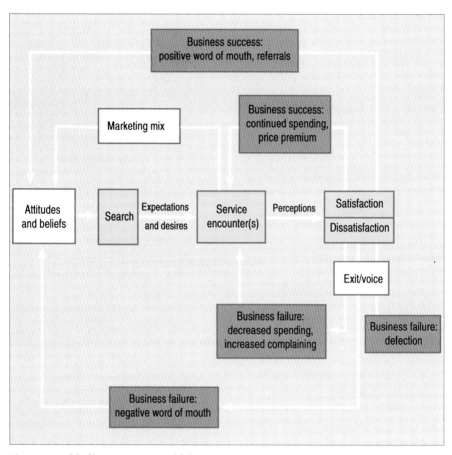

Fig. 1.1 A model of business success and failure.

A word of caution – patient care isn't enough

Satisfying your patients is a necessary but not a sufficient condition of competitive survival. You must still offer something that people want or need. It is no use applying state-of-the-art principles of customer care if all you can offer in the way of treatment is extractions and acrylic partial dentures. Unfortunately, companies often define their businesses in terms of the products they produce. But as Theodore Levitt (1960) showed in his classic article *Marketing Myopia*, this is a dangerous way to define a business. Products are

7

made obsolete by new technologies and changes in needs. To prevent the company becoming obsolete, Levitt proposed that companies should define themselves in terms of the customers' needs they serve rather than the products they sell. Witness the company that made the best slide rules in the world but went out of business when the first electronic calculators appeared on the market – the business should have been described as calculation, not slide rules. As dentists we should not define ourselves by the products we offer (crowns, veneers and so on) but rather by the needs of our patients. In both business and professional senses dentistry should be defined much more in terms of a service dedicated to the creation of wellness and improved quality of life for patients and less as the 'manufacture' of technical items – an approach that has tended to dominate thinking in the past.

Chapters 2 and 3 explore the implication of treating dentistry as a service-oriented operation, firstly in the way patients select a dental practice and secondly, on the important issue of patient loyalty. It must be stressed that while service quality can be split into two components, technical quality (the core service or product) and process quality (customer care concepts and techniques), excellence in this latter area simply cannot compensate for weaknesses in technical quality. The secret, obvious though it may be, is to combine excellent patient care with excellent technical treatment. The principles behind the attainment of excellent patient care are simple; following through with them is the hard part.

Chapter 4 highlights the importance of winning the hearts and minds of your staff in achieving high levels of patient satisfaction. Chapter 5 explores ways of gathering and using feedback about your practice and shows that questionnaires, while useful, aren't always the best way of finding out what your patients really think of you. Finally, Chapter 6 examines the issue of patient dissatisfaction more closely and looks at ways of turning it to your advantage.

Summary

- Patient satisfaction is a necessary prerequisite for business success in dental practice.
- The consequences of patient dissatisfaction are extremely damaging to a practice.
- Excellent patient care is not enough; a range of treatments that meet patients' needs must accompany it.

How do patients choose a dental practice?

An industry begins with the customer and his needs, not with a patent, a raw material, or a selling skill.

Theodore Levitt

Before we look at the way patients choose a dental practice, it is useful to look at some of the characteristics that differentiate buying and using a service (such as dentistry) from buying and using a product such as a can of baked beans. What exactly do we mean by the term 'service'? For many years the tendency has been to make a clear distinction between businesses and organisations that produce tangible goods (manufacturing), and those in which the 'product' is less tangible (service). Traditionally this has been expressed as 'manufacturing equals things' and 'services equal people'. Current thinking, however, holds that almost every activity includes some element of service and that the distinction between service and manufacturing has, in most cases, become rather blurred. Some people would even go as far as saying that there is no such thing as a 'service industry' and that there are only industries whose service components are greater or less than those of other industries. All that said, an awareness of the intrinsic characteristics of services (and their implications for management) helps provide us as dentists with a greater understanding of why things happen in our practices the way they do and, more significantly, why people behave the way they do. The key differences between services and products are described below along with the resulting managerial implications.

Nature of the product
Goods have been described as 'an object, a device, a thing', in contrast to a service which is a 'deed, a performance, an effort.' While services usually include tangible aspects – the meal in a restaurant, the crowns and bridges we place – the service itself is basically intangible.
Result: Managing (planning, operating and marketing) a performance is very

9

different from managing a physical object.

Customers are present in the service system

A service usually involves contact between the customer and the organisation – the customer may be present within, or have access to, the service system. Customers are often encouraged to become involved in the creation of the service product by co-operating with service personnel in settings such as hair salons, hotels and hospitals.

Result: Not only is the service system visible to the customer, the customer is also a 'resource' to be managed.

People as part of the product

Most services are the result of an interaction between the customer and a contact worker. The result of person-to-person contact may well vary from day to day, from server to server and from customer to customer.

Result: The difference between two service businesses usually rests in the quality of the employees who deliver the service.

Quality control

While manufactured goods can be checked for conformance to quality standards, services are generally consumed as they are produced. This, together with the aforementioned intangibility and human element, means that errors and deficiencies occur more easily and are often more difficult to conceal. Such unpredictability and heterogeneity is exacerbated by the presence of service personnel and other customers.

Result: Service organisations find it difficult to control quality and to offer customers a consistent product.

Perishability

Since a service is a deed or a performance, rather than a tangible item the customer keeps, it cannot be stored. While equipment and personnel can be ready and waiting to provide the service, these only represent the potential productive capacity. Customers must be present for the system to work. An empty airline seat cannot be put into storage. It is either filled for the flight or it remains empty. Conversely, when demand exceeds capacity, customers are likely to be sent away disappointed as no back up is available.

Result: Service managers must try to smooth demand levels to match capacity.

The time factor
There are limits to how long customers are willing to be kept waiting for the service to be provided. Furthermore, customers do not expect to spend longer receiving the service than appears reasonable to them.
Result: As far as customers are concerned, services are delivered in 'real time'.

Channels of distribution
Unlike manufacturing firms, service operations do not require physical distribution channels for moving goods from the factory to the consumer.
Result: Service businesses combine the service factory, retail outlet and point of consumption into one.
It is clear that dentistry in all its various guises bears most of the hallmarks of a service operation. While some manufacturing does occur – crowns and dentures are obvious tangible examples of our work – much of dentistry comprises aspects that cannot be so easily quantified. It is this very intangibility that makes choosing a dentist such a difficult task for most people. They may try to overcome this intrinsic predicament by, consciously or subconsciously, carrying out a series of actions.

The decision-making process

The process by which a person chooses a particular service or product is an integral part of a longer sequence of events commonly referred to as the 'decision-making process', a process that is at the very heart of modern consumer behaviour theory. It comprises the following five steps.

• Need recognition.
• Information search.
• Evaluation of alternatives.
• Purchase.
• Purchase outcome.

This chapter explores the first three of these steps in relation to dental practice.

11

Step 1 – Need recognition

Need recognition occurs when a person sees a significant difference between their existing situation and some desired or ideal state. A person's needs are extremely wide ranging and vary in their severity. Few dental problems would seem to fit into the most basic category of physical needs essential to life and survival. However, anything that stirs up sufficient emotion inside a patient's mind to make them overcome a host of fears and anxieties and contact a dentist should not be dismissed lightly. Patients can turn up with an almost endless variety of needs, not just obvious treatment needs but also a more subtle range of psychological needs.

Treatment needs
As far as treatment is concerned, patients rarely request a specific item of treatment; rather they are seeking a solution to a problem that they see as being detrimental to their well being. Whichever treatment option is chosen, the number one priority is that it must be seen by the patient to have satisfied that primary need. Clearly, unrealistic patient expectations need to be balanced against practical possibility. Nevertheless, how often do we assume that we know what patients expect rather than really take the time to find out? Identifying patient expectations of the benefits to be gained from treatment is a vital task for any dentist keen on trying to satisfy those patients. If nothing else, it is important to protect yourself against possible litigation. Dental Protection Ltd recently highlighted, for example, the potential danger of imaging techniques creating in the patient's mind unrealistic expectations. When the treatment outcome expected by the patient fails to materialise , he or she is likely to experience intense dissastisfaction and in some cases this difference between concept and reality is the vacuum within which complaints and even litigation can arise.

Psychological needs
These are, by their very nature, more abstract than the patient's physical demands. By recognising the patient's psychological needs you are more likely to make that all-important good first impression. William Martin, author of *Quality Customer Service for Front Line Staff*, has described four basic patient needs that you and your staff must look out for and pay close attention to.

• The need to be understood. Patients should be made to feel that they are communicating effectively, and that the messages they send are being interpreted correctly. This need is signalled by customers repeating themselves, speaking slowly and/or loudly, getting angry when they are not being understood, or bringing a friend or relative to help explain.

- The need to feel welcome. Any patient who is made to feel like an outsider will probably not return. Patients need to feel that you are happy to see them and their patronage is important to you.
- The need to feel important. Ego and self-esteem are powerful human needs. Everyone likes to feel important and so you should do anything you can to make patients feel special.
- The need for comfort. This need is expressed by customers who are ill at ease, nervous or unsure of themselves and is therefore a given for most dental patients! But this is more than just the absence of physical pain and discomfort during treatment. Patients also need psychological comfort, the assurance that they will be taken care of properly, and the confidence that you will meet their needs.

You cannot address these needs without correctly 'reading' your patients by being sensitive to the verbal and non-verbal signals being sent out. In particular, you and your staff must be good listeners. It has been said that the most important activity any business can do is listen to its customers and so it is vital that you observe the following.

- Stop talking and allow the other person time to answer. Research has shown that patients discuss their medical concerns for an average of 18 seconds before health-care providers interrupt them.
- Don't be defensive.
- Avoid distractions, so that you can concentrate on the other person and look for the 'real' meaning in what they say.
- Provide feedback to show the patient that you have understood.

Steps 2 and 3 – Information search and Evaluation of alternatives

Once the patient has identified a problem that needs to be solved, they may or may not search for more information on how best to tackle that problem. The amount of time and effort invested in the search process is termed 'involvement'. For some people the drive to find out more is strong and so they will exert a great deal of time and energy into the process of searching for a dentist. Other people behave in exactly the opposite way and rely on whatever information is stored in their memory. In the middle are the majority of patients who want to feel that they are making a realistic, informed choice about which dentist to visit.

Consumer information search is one of the most widely studied areas in the field of consumer research, with literature on the subject dating back to 1917. Most of this research has been conducted in the field of consumer products. These are, in the main, tangible items characterised by 'search qualities' – attributes which a consumer can determine prior to purchase. Search qualities include features such as colour, style, price, fit, feel, hardness and smell. Some goods (eg clothing, furniture and jewelry) are high in search qualities as their attributes can be almost completely determined and evaluated prior to purchase. In addition, 'experience qualities' comprise those attributes that can only be discerned after purchase or during consumption. Many goods and services (eg package holidays and restaurant meals) are high in such experience qualities since their attributes cannot be known or assessed until they have been purchased and are being consumed.

A third category, that of 'credence qualities', includes those characteristics that the consumer may find impossible to evaluate even after purchase and consumption. For example, many medical operations and car repairs can be said to be high in credence qualities since few consumers possess medical or mechanical skills sufficient to evaluate whether these services are necessary or are performed properly, even after they have been prescribed and produced by the seller. Figure 2.1 shows a continuum of evaluation that incorporates these ideas.

At the left end of the continuum are goods high in search qualities and, accordingly, easiest to evaluate even before purchase. In the centre are goods and services high in experience qualities, more difficult to evaluate because they must be purchased and consumed before assessment is possible. At the right end of the continuum are goods and services high in credence qualities, most difficult to evaluate because the consumer may be unaware of, or may lack sufficient knowledge to determine, whether the offerings satisfy given wants or needs, even after consumption. Most consumer goods fall to the left of this continuum, while most services fall to the right. The very nature of services, for example their intangibility and non-standardisation, make them that much more difficult to evaluate than goods. All this difficulty understandably heightens prepurchase uncertainty. It also means that the most likely sources of information used by

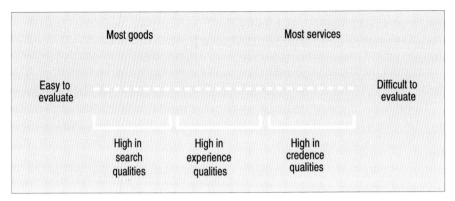

Fig. 2.1 The continuum of product and service evaluation.

patients are the vicarious experiences and opinions of other individuals. While such information is subjective, it nevertheless goes a long way towards reducing uncertainty as it approximates direct experience with the service.

The search process and dental practice

The research that has been done on customer information search with respect to dental practices confirms that patients rely heavily on the opinions of others when deciding which practice to visit. As is commonly the case, much of this research has been conducted in the USA; nevertheless it seems reasonable to assume that in general the same findings apply to the UK. Most studies conclude that patients seeking dental care prefer to consult personal sources of information (family, friends and work colleagues) rather than non-personal ones (advertisements, phone lists, etc). These studies go on to stress the importance of fostering good relationships with current patients. There is little doubt that because of the experiential nature of the service people feel less at risk in selecting a dentist if they are using a personal referral.

The exact proportion of new patients who come through personal recommendation is to some extent influenced by the marketing mix of the particular practice. The marketing mix is classically summarised by the four Ps of product, price, place and promotion, and the balance of these four factors signals the offer being made to the consumer. For new patients, all these factors come into play when deciding whether or not to visit a particular dentist. The one aspect of the marketing mix that new patients, for the most part, find

15

impossible to evaluate is the product, ie the actual treatment itself. Therefore, the other three components of the marketing mix (together with word of mouth from family and friends) are used as surrogates for treatment quality. Thus, patients like to have information about the likely cost of treatment. The location and external physical appearance of the practice should give a clear indication of what goes on inside, as should any promotional activities carried out by the practice. Promotion in this sense is taken to cover more than just obvious physical promotional materials such as practice brochures, advertisements, etc and includes, for example, telephone manner in terms of the efficiency, courtesy and empathy of practice staff when dealing with requests for information.

After personal recommendation, convenient location is usually the next most important factor used by patients with the physical location and appearance of the practice creating an impression of the service to be expected by the patient. Studies have shown that a dentist might be perceived as being the most competent in the area, but a poor location or an unattractive appearance may lead patients not to select that practitioner.

A related factor, and one that is often ignored, is the presence and nature of other patients attending the practice. Research has shown that people believe that too many patients waiting in the reception area indicates over-booking and therefore poor service. Conversely, seeing no patients indicates possible inferior quality of service ('this dentist can't be any good'). In addition, the type of patient present in the waiting room can also be used as a cue to service quality. A respondent in one study, for example, stated that a physician whose patients look like winos 'couldn't be any good'.

It is clear that patients may struggle to decide which dentist to go to in the first place. However, once they have started to accumulate their own experiences of that dentist they begin to gain more confidence in their own ability to judge the quality of care being provided and these judgements then tend to dominate in the future. All this was neatly summarised by one lady taking part in a focus group I conducted recently.

> *The ones I tried since I moved here were through personal recommendation, but I just didn't have the same confidence. One of them still had one of these drills that sort of hung down and it was awful because it wasn't high speed so it's much more uncomfortable. So I now travel back over there to see the one I used to go to.*

A word or two on advertising

When the regulations concerning dental advertising were relaxed during the 1980s there were considerable worries expressed in some quarters of the profession about the dire consequences that would ensue as a result of deregulation. Nowadays, there is little such concern and indeed there is perhaps a growing view that advertising may even avoid some of the misunderstandings that lead to dissatisfaction in that the more the patient knows about what to expect, the fewer unpleasant shocks and surprises they will receive. For this scenario to be reality it is vital to deliver what is promised, even to the extent of under-promising so that over-delivering becomes easier.

In large organisations matching what is delivered with what is promised can be problematic since the marketing department might not clearly understand the actual levels of service delivery. A famous example is that of Domino's Pizza who scrapped their thirty-minute delivery guarantee in 1993 after an American jury awarded $79 million to a woman injured by an 18-year-old Domino's driver who ignored a red light. Other injuries, and even a few deaths, had been blamed on the guarantee, which proved just too difficult to achieve consistently. This lack of mutual understanding is clearly less likely to happen in most dental practices where the marketing department and the operations manager are usually one and the same person! Nevertheless the principle still exists – to be appropriate and effective, communications about service quality must accurately reflect what the customer will actually receive in the service encounter, even if this means resetting patient expectations to more realistic levels.

Dentistry on the Internet

There are already signs that the Internet, albeit in its infancy, is increasingly being used to help patients in their choice of dentist, either through dentists' own web-pages, 'find a dentist' schemes or a combination of the two. It is also a useful information source for patients who can access a whole range of web sites aimed at informing the public on current dental treatments, eg www.bda-dentistry.org.uk.

Why is the Internet so effective? The main reason is that you are never going to get more attention from a potential patient than when they are online. Both their hands are on the keyboard and both their eyes are on the monitor. You are interacting with them. They have preselected you. They want to see you. A further advantage is the Internet's ability to provide considerable amounts of factual information about a practice, its staff and the services offered.

There are some words of caution though. We are now in an era where most Internet Service Providers offer a free web page template. These designs are fairly basic, even rudimentary, but why should that matter? It is free after all. The problem is that if you want your practice to look like all the others on the Internet go ahead, but one of the key rules of marketing is to be able to tell your customers how you are different and better than your competitors. That is very difficult to do if your site looks and feels like everyone else's. The value of a professionally designed web site cannot be over-estimated – as with any type of advertising medium, one size does not fit all.

The problem with most information posted on dental practice web sites is that it is rarely reinforced by independent word of mouth and, as already stated, this is what patients prefer to rely on when choosing a practice. The end result is that patients' perceptions of risk remain high. So, even if a patient makes use of a 'find a dentist' service it is still likely that that the patient will engage in further word of mouth information-seeking activities to strengthen the conviction that this is indeed the dentist to go to. It seems to make sense for dental practice web sites to use patient testimonials as a way of overcoming this problem. As Dan Janal (2000) writes in his book *Marketing on the Internet*:

> On the web, no one really knows who you are or how credible you are. Testimonials can bridge the gap. However a simple "I like the product" will not win many new sales. For testimonials to be effective they must have several elements and you must employ several strategies to get them.

Janal believes that testimonials should be pursued quite aggressively since people probably won't write them unless you ask. They should include the patient's full name, cover a range of professions and be written in the patient's own words. He also recommends checking e-mails and other correspondence for unsolicited testimonials. If such testimonials are to be used, it makes sense to ask the writer's permission to use his or her words on the internet.

Whatever promotional medium is used always remember that spirit, energy, personality, warmth, friendliness and honesty will always work. Choosing a dentist is a difficult task for most new patients. You should do all you can to make that task easier by encouraging your existing patients to spread the good news about your practice – in other words to become your ambassadors. Try

18

and make the intangible tangible. Give out as much information as you can and pay just as much attention to the presentation of that information as you do to the content. Most of all ensure that all members of your staff exude a friendly, confident and caring attitude at all times.

Summary

- Patient needs are diverse and must be clearly identified if they are to be fulfilled.
- Like many other services, dentistry is high in experience and credence qualities that make it difficult for patients to make valid prepurchase evaluations.
- Personal referral sources tend to dominate the initial selection process followed by factors found in the four Ps marketing mix such as product, price, place and promotional activities.
- Subsequent service delivery and the nature of care given, as perceived by the patient, determines future patronage.
- Advertising must not over-promise – always ensure that you can do what you say you can do. Content should reflect the practice's fundamental personality and honesty.

Why patients stay loyal to a dental practice

3

The business world rediscovered customers in the 1980s. Companies proclaimed themselves customer focused. Often this involved sending a receptionist on a customer care course, promising to answer the telephone within five rings and smiling a lot. It was hoped the end result would be customer delight, legions of happy customers who would return time and time again. A small number of companies got it right. But these were largely the companies who had never forgotten their customers in the first place. The rest were left with a smile on their face.

Stuart Crainer, business writer

Attracting new patients is only the first step – keeping hold of them, making sure they don't drift away or, even worse, defect to another practice is critical and should occupy the thoughts of everyone working in the practice. If patient loyalty is the cornerstone of business success and the ways recommended to achieve it largely commonsense, why is it that so many practices seem to experience such considerable difficulty in attaining it? Perhaps the problem is that, while the methods may appear simple, putting them into practice consistently appears to be rather more difficult. The difficulty lies in the fact that people are an integral part of the dental product and yet they invariably behave differently from day to day and in different situations. The dentist, however, who works out how to harness the collective genius of the people in his or her practice will more than likely be extremely successful.

Patients don't need much of an excuse to avoid going to the dentist. In spite of the wonders of modern dentistry the whole process remains something that the vast majority of people endure rather than enjoy. Accordingly, dentistry isn't usually top of most consumers' wish list. Let's face it, it usually takes a lot for someone to come and see us the first time. Accordingly, new patients are in a state of heightened awareness and so you should look on them as human sponges soaking up all that you and your staff say and do. New patients are precious commodities to be meticulously nurtured – they have the power to make or break you. This is not to say that existing patients don't matter, nothing could be further from the truth, it's just that longstanding patients are more likely to forgive the occasional minor negative incident and stay loyal. So, is patient loyalty just a matter of avoiding negative incidents? In a sense yes or at least it is an essential prerequisite. In a sense yes or at least it is an essential prerequisite, so much so that the first priority should be to eliminate all those situations that could lead to dissatisfaction, as these are the situations that cause patients to jump ship. Only then can you get on with satisfying and delighting them.

So what are these negative incidents that might cause patients to express dissatisfaction? Notice the word 'might' in that sentence because, as we shall see in Chapter 6, negative incidents don't always lead to dissatisfaction, the key is in how you or your staff handle such situations. To the patient, negative incidents are those events that do not match their own preconceived ideas of the level of care and service that they feel should be provided for them. In other words, if we don't match their expectations there is a strong possibility that they will not be happy. In consumer management terms this is explained by disconfirmation theory. This theory proposes that consumer satisfaction is related to the size and direction of disconfirmation (Figure 3.1), which is defined as the difference between an individual's prepurchase expectations and their postpurchase assessment of the product or service.

The following conversation is typical.

'When I had my wisdom teeth out nobody told me that I was going to be in absolute agony and bleeding for days and days. I was devastated. I had arranged to go out with my friends the night after I'd had it done but I ended up with a bag of frozen peas stuck to my face for about a fortnight. Nobody warned me that it was going to be so bad.'

'If you had been warned would you still have gone through with it?'

'Yes, definitely, yes because I was in pain with them and so I knew it had to be done. I wanted to be prepared for it and I just wasn't, I was totally unprepared for what happened.'

You could argue that this patient was a little naive in her expectations, but that would be missing the point altogether. Those were her expectations and they were very real to her. Whatever we or anybody else might have believed in that situation is immaterial. Her expectations, however misguided, were not matched and not surprisingly she was dissatisfied.

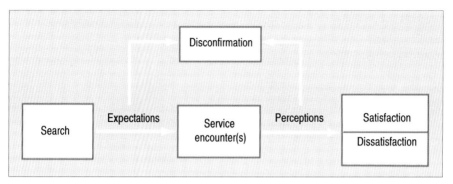

Fig. 3.1 Disconfirmation theory of customer satisfaction.

A further factor, that of fairness or equity, is also thought to play a significant role in shaping satisfaction. The importance of fairness in dealings with the dentist was made by another patient:

'One thing that happens when you are in the waiting room, and I think it happens at a lot of dentists, is that they make appointments for people at the same time. For example, at two o'clock there can be up to eight people waiting and everybody is looking and wondering 'well I wonder what time her appointment is?' or 'he got here after me but he's being seen before me.' The last time I went, one guy got up and stormed out. He'd watched four people go in although his appointment was at two o'clock. I told the receptionist they shouldn't do that, it's unfair.'

In Chapter 2, the observation was made in that service performance is variable. The way that consumers recognise and are willing to accept this variation is explained using the 'zone of tolerance' concept (Figure 3.2).

In theory, predicted service could equate with either desired or adequate service but is most likely to fall between the two and hence within the zone of tolerance. The zone of tolerance is seen as the range or window in which customers do not particularly notice service performance. When performance falls outside the range, ie service is either very good or very poor, the customer expresses satisfaction or dissatisfaction. Customer tolerance zones are thought to vary for different service attributes and the more important the factor, the narrower the zone of tolerance is likely to be. Figure 3.2 illustrates the likely difference between the most important factors (eg service outcome – the result of the service) and the least important ones (eg service process – the way the service is delivered). The first step then in our quest to satisfy our patients is to

23

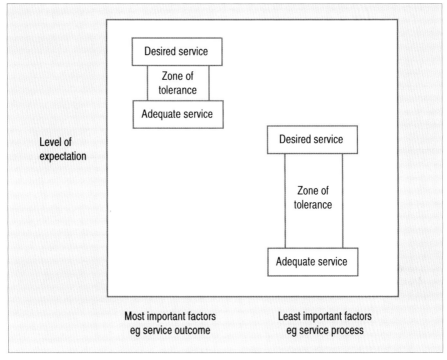

Fig. 3.2 Zone of tolerance.

recognise that we have to at least match their various expectations and aspirations. The more we fall short of these, the more likely that patients will be dissatisfied. Every patient comes with a ready-made cocktail of expectations and desires concerning the service they are about to receive. But how are these expectations formed and, perhaps more importantly, can they be influenced?

Expectations and desires

It is generally held that expectations and desires arise from attitudes moulded by social background, previous experiences, word of mouth from family and friends and to some extent the marketing efforts of the provider (Figure 3.3).

Of these various factors, clearly you as an individual dentist can do very little to influence either demographic factors or previous experiences at other dentists. Where you do have considerable ability to influence patients is, of

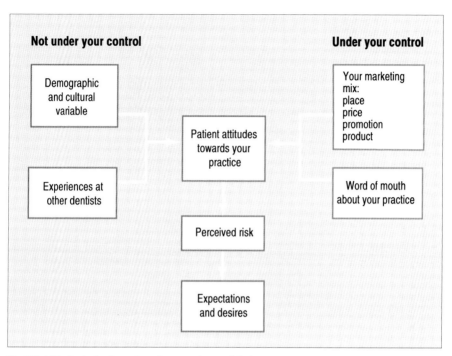

Not under your control

Demographic
and cultural
variable

Experiences at
other dentists

Patient attitudes
towards your
practice

Perceived risk

Expectations
and desires

Under your control

Your marketing
mix:
place
price
promotion
product

Word of mouth
about your practice

Fig. 3.3 Attitudes in the formation of expectations and desires.

course, with respect to the experiences they have at your practice. These experiences impact directly on patient loyalty and on the magnitude and nature of word of mouth passed on to others. They arise from the marketing strategies that wittingly, or unwittingly, you adopt in the practice. For many people marketing is synonymous with advertising, mail shots, etc. In truth, it embraces far more than that – remember the four Ps, a combination of strategies all aimed at addressing the needs and desires of the consumer. For example, take the case on page 22 of the patient with problems after wisdom tooth extraction. It is likely that her expectations could have been moulded into something much closer to reality had anyone taken the time to sit down with her, find out what she expected to happen and then explain the likely outcome. That is marketing.

We keep coming back to the central theme of this book – that the level of perceived risk is far greater when purchasing services rather than goods, especially when that service provider is being used for the first time. This applies even more so to professional services such as dentistry because few consumers possess the necessary skills needed to evaluate whether the service has been performed properly – even after it has been prescribed and 'produced'. Objective assessment of technical quality is clearly a difficult, if not impossible, task for most patients. Even dentists cannot always agree amongst themselves just what constitutes quality dentistry. It is little wonder then that patients use other parameters, ones that they can understand as a measure of our performance. Some of the factors commonly assessed by patients include the following.

- Cues   What do I think of the physical evidence of service?
- Comfort   Was the treatment painful or uncomfortable?
- Convenience   Could I organise my visits at times that were
                      convenient for me?
- Care   Was I made to feel their number one priority?
- Communication   Was everything fully explained to me?
- Courtesy   Was I treated fairly and with respect?
- Cost   Did I receive value for money?

Patient perceptions of these parameters are critical antecedents of satisfaction and hence patient loyalty. It follows that how you manage and influence them will play a key role in ensuring the commercial success (or failure) of your practice.

Patient perceptions: process versus technical quality

In general, people appraise the quality of services firstly, on the outcome of any technical work (technical quality) and secondly, on the way that this technical work was delivered (process quality). If the service has a specific technical outcome, for example a lawyer winning or losing an important case, then the effectiveness of the service rendered can be evaluated purely on the basis of the outcome. Similar situations arise in dental practice, particularly where the outcome is the resolution of an acute problem. Problem solving is perhaps the factor most closely linked to the dentist's technical competence, although the two are by no means synonymous. Patients do look favourably upon dentists who they perceive to have resolved their clinical problems.

'A good dentist is a good witchdoctor. You go to the dentist with a toothache and you come out and the toothache or the abscess has gone and you don't feel any discomfort and you think well…he's alright.'

However, much of the work carried out by professional service providers, including dentists, is highly complex and a clear outcome is not always evident. In these situations judging the technical quality of the service is not always easy. For example, many patients may never know for sure whether their particular root canal treatment was performed correctly, or even if it was needed in the first place. The existence of both process and technical quality can explain why dentists with superb technical skills often fail to compete effectively with dentists who are less skilled but who deliver superior interpersonal quality. If patients do not feel capable of judging effectively the technical quality of the outcome they are likely to base their quality judgements on a number of process quality dimensions.

Reliability: delivering on promises
Patients want practices to keep their promises – promises about appointment times, problem resolution, pain control, cost of treatment and so on. If you can't keep a promise, don't make it. If you say you are going to phone someone, make sure you do. Think about those companies that you keep on going back to, again and again. Unless you have no choice about which you do business with, it is likely that those companies you are most loyal to are reliable in delivering their core service.

Responsiveness: being willing to help
This dimension emphasises attentiveness and promptness in dealing with patient requests, questions, complaints and problems. Most importantly, for dentists it means a willingness to listen. Responsiveness is communicated to patients by such things as the length of time they have to wait to be seen after they have called in pain, for answers to questions or attention to problems. Responsiveness also captures the notion of flexibility and ability to customise the service to the needs of the patient.

Empathy: treating patients as individuals
The essence of empathy is conveying, through personalised or customised service, that patients are unique or special. This means putting yourself in the position of your patients. You and your staff must view any given situation through their eyes, ie, 'If I were this patient what would I want?' As a simple example, when the dental chair goes back patients often feel vulnerable and powerless. This is a good time to reassure the patient and concentrate on them and not on trying to do something else.

Similarly, reception staff should do all they can to greet patients by name and build relationships that reflect personal knowledge of their requirements and preferences. Remember that people want to know how much you care before they care about how much you know. One of the best ways to demonstrate this concern is to make same-day phone calls to all those patients who have undergone 'invasive' treatment. Just ask how they are. This expression of concern for their well being is almost guaranteed to yield extremely positive responses from patients.

Appearances: personnel, physical facilities, equipment and promotional materials

Because so much of dentistry is intangible, patients, especially new ones, often rely on tangible cues, the physical 'evidence' of service in other words, to assist them in evaluating us before, during and after treatment – if it looks right it probably is. Everything from the external appearance of the practice, signage, interior design and ambience, equipment and even air quality and temperature all act as factors in the patient's quality evaluation. Staff uniforms, practice stationery and brochures clearly impact on the patient and yet these are so often over-looked or ill conceived. In the management literature the physical facility where service is performed, delivered and consumed is termed the servicescape. Retailers know all too well that customers are influenced by such things as smell, decor, music and store layout and it can be a challenge to design this physical space to match the needs and preferences of both consumers and employees. For example, consumers may perceive they are paying for expensive décor whereas employees may perceive an investment in the environment as an indication of the management's concern for their job satisfaction.

Assurance: inspiring trust and confidence

Last, but most definitely not least, this dimension of process quality is vitally important for those services that are seen as 'high risk' and difficult to evaluate. Time and time again, patients who are happy with the service they receive will very often talk of the 'confidence' and 'trust' instilled by their dentist. While a new patient may use word of mouth and tangible evidence (such as visible evidence of degrees, honours and awards) to make a provisional assessment of this dimension, the only way to develop trust is through one's actions. Inspiring trust and confidence is really the sum of the previous four factors. In other words, it springs from the ability of practice staff to communicate to the patient their reliability, responsiveness and empathy.

These various dimensions of process quality are used by patients to signal the presence or absence of technical quality and an awareness and understanding of them allows dentists some control over their patients' perceptions and therefore the extent of their satisfaction. Unfortunately, various studies have highlighted the substantial gap that can often exist between patients' expectations and dentists' understanding of those expectations. Burke and Croucher for example, asked patients to evaluate 16 criteria of 'good practice'. Eight criteria were proposed by dentists and eight by patients. The three ranked highest by patients were explanation of procedures, sterilisation/hygiene and dentists' skills (all criteria proposed by patients). The three ranked lowest were up-to-date equipment, pleasant décor and good practice image (all criteria proposed by dentists). All this does rather suggest that dentists mistakenly believe they know what patients want, rather than finding out what they actually do want.

Patient fees and satisfaction

The subject of money has, almost inevitably, the ability to cast a dark cloud over any relationship. Dentistry is no different and if you want your patients to think how wonderful you are you must communicate effectively with them on this thorny but crucial issue. When patients are asked about 'money and dentists' the first thing they will probably talk about is how expensive modern dentistry is and how rich dentists are. Even famed restaurateur Sir Terence Conran recently observed, 'When you think what the restaurateur has to do for the £25 or £30 you're paying, compared to what you pay a dentist'. Nevertheless, patients usually appreciate that we are providing a modern, highly skilled service and that any such professional service doesn't come cheap – just ask your patients how they feel about the fees charged by lawyers! In fact, it is rarely the out and out cost of treatment that causes headaches for patients. The actual cost of treatment is for many people one of the least important of the considerations involved in selecting a dentist. The real value of cost is that patients use it as an indicator of quality. In other words, a patient who has perceived the quality of care to be high will interpret the prices as fair. Those patients who think that a dentist's fees are too high tend to be those patients who are also dissatisfied with the quality of care provided.

The big problem is our inability as a profession to explain fully, before treatment, the financial implications of treatment. We also often fail to convince patients of the justification for the enormous variety of fees charged by different dentists. The more I talk to patients the more I realise that this is the area that we as dentists leave most to be desired. Time and again I hear comments such as these.

- You never get to know beforehand how much it's going to cost. It would be nice to have a basic idea. By the time you have opened your mouth and he says you need this that and the other and you have no idea what the charges are for a clean-up or a filling or a crown.
- They are not used to being pinned down are they? I wonder how many times people actually ask them 'What exactly am I paying for?' I bet they are not used to that. You are in there and you don't get a chance to have a chat with them do you?
- There was a programme on the television and it was talking about different dentists and their charges ranged from, and I can't remember what the treatment was, but the lowest was something like £200 and the highest £900. The reporter had gone to seven or eight different dentists around the country. When you start hearing stories like that you start getting sceptical about it all, don't you?

The message comes across loud and clear. We are charging what is perceived to be a relatively high price for what we do and patients feel they have a right to know what that price is before they can consider making a rational decision. Few of us would go ahead and buy a new car without giving any consideration to its price, and yet that is so often what we expect patients to do with respect to their treatment. Equally, just because you or I might feel that our fee for say a prophylaxis is negligible doesn't mean that the patient can dismiss that cost so lightly. Often the main gripe for many patients is the dentist's reluctance to say in advance what the fee will be. This is also linked to a fear of exploitation, ignorance of the overall level of charge and anger about the way that the final bill is presented. Added to this, patients are often confused about whether the completion of a course of treatment carries with it any form of guaranteed dental fitness for the next six months.

Patients resent being kept in the dark about the cost implications of their treatment. How can we begin to perform reliably, keep our promises in other words, if we don't make that promise in the first place? Clear communication about money is vital if you want to avoid what will be inevitable problems further down the line.

Summary

- Satisfaction is a balance between patients' a) desires and perceptions of the dentist's duty and b) perceptions of what the dentist actually does.
- The 'zone of tolerance' falls between desired and adequate service. Only service that falls outside this zone tends to get noticed.
- Dentists can exert most influence on patient expectations through the quality of service they provide.
- Patients have difficulty in assessing the technical quality of a dentist's work and so they rely on the assessment of the characteristics of process quality, including reliability, responsiveness, empathy, tangible cues and assurance.
- Adequate discussion of fees is a critical factor in preventing patient dissatisfaction.

The importance of teamwork

4

> *We simply do not believe that our employees have an interest in coming in late, leaving early, and doing as little as possible for as much money as they can wheedle out of us. They are adults. At Semco we treat them like adults. We trust them. We get out of their way and let them do their jobs.*

> Ricardo Semler, Chief Executive, Semco

Why satisfying your staff is as important as satisfying your patients

The people who work in an organisation are its lifeblood; its heart and soul. This is true for any business, but particularly so for service organisations. Remember, two of the chief characteristics of services are that people are part of the product and that, for most of the time, customers are present in the system. Competing providers may offer the same types of service, be they preparation of tax returns, cut and blow-dry or scale and polish, but they do not provide the same quality of service. No one knows this better than our own patients. To them, competing service enterprises may look alike, but they certainly don't feel the same. Service quality has become the great differentiator; the most powerful competitive weapon service organisations possess. The £10 notes a customer receives from the tellers in four competing banks are the same – it is the tellers that are different.

You should look on your staff as being your most valuable asset. No single aspect of your practice is more important, demands more of your time and energy and is a more integral part of your success. Patients don't usually come to a particular practice because it has just installed a new computer system. Of course this might improve the service, but, as we keep saying over and over again, people come because of the way they are treated as human beings. It should come as no surprise then that numerous studies have shown that employee satisfaction is a necessary prerequisite of customer satisfaction. If members of your staff are lacking in motivati on, do not enjoy their work and merely tolerate their choice of employment, then it is highly unlikely that they will give your patients the requisite care, attention and wholehearted enthusiasm. With the best will in the world, disgruntled and disharmonious staff cannot, and do not, exude the passion for excellence in their work that will make patients really sit up and notice.

Patients quickly feel tension among staff and staff problems quickly become patient problems. Patients also like continuity, not having to forge new relationships every time they come. They want to know that we care about their likes and dislikes, simply that we know them – no one wants to be referred to as the 'one-hour crown prep'. The highest compliment a patient can give to practice staff is to say that they make them feel like part of the 'family'. Such continuity and sense of community can only come from staff who are happy and fulfilled in their jobs and who, to use a rather well-worn cliché, are all singing from the same sheet of music.

It follows that if patient satisfaction springs largely from employee satisfaction then the latter is an important factor driving profitability. In his article *Common traits of the million dollar practice*, consultant Robert Hamric's (1996) top four factors are all staff related – as he says: 'You will never see a million-dollar practice without a million-dollar staff'. The financial benefits of satisfied staff include the following.

- Your staff are, in many ways, closer than you to the 'front line' and therefore often understand better what needs to be done to improve the service offered. The more committed and motivated they are the more likely they will actively look for ways of improving the service.
- Satisfied, motivated staff are more likely to take on greater responsibilities leaving you to do a whole range of other, more productive, asks. The more of these other responsibilities that you can delegate to your staff the easier your life will be and the more profitable your practice.
- If you look after your employees you will not have such a high staff turnover and will therefore be in a position to take on new staff as and when it suits you.

Last but not least, there is the simple feel good factor of working in a team of people who enjoy their work and who enjoy spending their working lives in each other's company.

Dentists and their staff – the sad reality

So, there are a host of good reasons why it makes a great deal of sense to employ and retain staff who are as motivated as they are skilled. Most dentists appreciate this and yet many have great difficulty achieving it. This is hardly a new phenomenon. As long ago as 1924, one Juliette Southard wrote in the *Journal of the American Dental Association*:

> *...the average dentist fails to consider seriously one of the most essential factors to his success, namely the proper selection of an efficient assistant.*

We can take some heart from the fact that most professional service providers find themselves in exactly the same position. Managing staff has been likened to herding cats; when they leave each night there is no guarantee they will be back the next day. More than in any other industry, professional service firms must create an environment in which employees are constantly motivated and can effectively balance their commitment to the practice and to the client as well as to themselves. And yet it has been shown that for a great many dentists, management is an area of their practice they rate as not being very satisfying and one that is ranked low in comparison to other areas. Newly qualified dentists have been shown to rate it as one of the areas for which they are least prepared. What is especially of concern is that many ancillary staff do not rate their dentist bosses too highly when it comes to their management expertise. Several studies have shown, for example, that dentists' management skills are frequently mentioned as a major source of staff dissatisfaction and that one of the most important factors leading to job stress for dental surgery assistants is that of feeling undervalued by the dentist. We should all realise that effective communication and management skills employed by 'the boss' are likely to have an important and powerful effect in reducing such stress.

Further evidence comes from an important study conducted by Bader and Sams (1992) into the use of three well-known management techniques (job descriptions, performance reviews and staff meetings) in general dental practice. Of the dentists surveyed 62% made use of regularly scheduled staff meetings, 52% up-to-date job descriptions, and only 44% regularly scheduled performance appraisals. In addition, dentists tended to believe that sound management strategies were more prevalent in their practices than did their staff members. Staff members clearly disagreed with dentists' views that that the latter's supervisory style emphasised good interpersonal relations through clear communication, openness to discussing problems, shared understanding of purpose, balanced feedback and encouragement of creativity. For example, a high proportion of dentists indicated that they would thank team members for their efforts at the end of a tough day, while the most frequent response from staff members was that the dentist was likely to do or say nothing. All this would be of just passing interest if it were not for the fact that the extent to which dentists and staff members disagree about the use of management techniques is related to the general job satisfaction of these team members. Conclusion? The better the dentist's grasp of interpersonal management skills, the greater the staff satisfaction and hence the greater the likelihood of patients being satisfied. The remainder of this chapter explores the issues that need to be resolved to create strong synergy between practice staff (including the dentists), the practice philosophy and the way the practice is organised to deliver that philosophy.

Building a winning team

There is an old business parable about three stone cutters who were asked to describe their jobs. The first said that his job was to cut stones. The second said that he had developed a new technique to cut stones more efficiently. The third simply said, 'I build cathedrals.' Your aim should be a practice full of cathedral builders. Without your own vision, your own particular cathedral, how can you expect people to wholeheartedly come on board with you? Such a sense of mission is essentially an emotional feeling by the people in the organisation. An organisation must have an underlying ethos that will capture the emotional support of its people. Increasingly, practices that are successful and prosperous tend also to be those practices that not only articulate their goals in writing, but also and, most importantly, strive to meet them. It is easy to deride mission statements. We see them everywhere these days and if the truth were told they all tend to say the same thing. But they do serve as a starting point and without them it is almost impossible to implement the changes that are usually required to bring about true patient satisfaction. Really successful practices are those that turn abstract goals and ideas into reality.

An important first step towards building a winning team is therefore to define the way you want and expect things to be done in your practice. In other words you must establish your own individual organisational culture, once described as:

'The ideologies, beliefs and deep-set values which occur in all firms. They are the prescriptions for the ways in which people should work in those organisations.' Harrison, R.

So, if you see your practice simply as a place for you to repair teeth, then you will end up with a staff made up, not of cathedral builders, but of stone cutters. Once your own particular philosophy has been established, the next logical step is to design jobs that will appeal to the sort of people who, given the chance, will help you turn it into reality. Compared to drawing up strategies and philosophies, implementation is unglamorous and deadly dull. But a failure to implement is the reason why most business managers fail. As we keep saying the things that really matter might seem obvious in theory but extremely difficult to pull off in practice.

Quality jobs with achievable standards of excellence

So many dentists assume that staff know what their duties are, and yet in most practices such duties are never explicitly written down. Designing jobs that reflect your commitment to patient satisfaction as well as quality dentistry is paramount. Requirements include the following.

- The purpose of the job.
- An explanation of the person's duties.
- The general working conditions.
- How the job relates to those of other members of staff.
- The technical and service standards that apply to this job.

Standards need to cover both the technical and procedural aspects of a job as well as the interpersonal ones. Technical standards clearly have an impact upon patient satisfaction and if standards are written at all, it is usually technical ones. This is simply because dentists are already familiar with and understand what is involved in procedures such as sterilisation or radiography procedures and so find it easier to establish standards and criteria.

Clearly though, service-oriented standards carry just as much, if not more, weight when it comes to patient perceptions and yet this is an area that dentists are less familiar with and therefore such standards rarely, if ever, get written. Chapter 3 made the point that patients most often use a range of 'soft' interpersonal factors to evaluate the service you offer. How well you score with respect to these largely determines patient loyalty. It makes sense then to try and set service standards that reflect these factors and that establish targets towards which both you and your staff can work. For example, in terms of appearance, standards might revolve around the following issues.

• What should patients see when they approach one of your staff?
• How should staff members appear?
• How should staff members convey a positive attitude?

Similar guidelines can be developed for the other important areas described in Chapter 3 – reliability, responsiveness, empathy and assurance. William Martin (1989) in his book *Managing Quality Customer Service* provides a number of guidelines that should be kept in mind when creating such service standards, namely that that they are:

• Clear   precise in meaning.
• Concise   short and to the point.
• Observable   can be seen or measured.
• Realistic   practical and attainable.

Perhaps the most important consideration is the way such standards are developed and then applied. Many management texts say that the biggest advantage of such standards is that they send out a clear message to everyone in the practice that this is what doing a good job means to you. This does appear to make sense…up to a point. The problem is that this view sees the use of controls as a means of pushing people forward, whereas surely a self-propelled workforce would be far more preferable. It seems to make more sense to involve those staff already working in the practice in writing their own service standards. The end result of such participation is that staff feel much more comfortable with the ensuing specifications rather than being left with the feeling that the standards have been imposed upon them. Successful business people invariably surround themselves with people who aspire to take responsibility. Once they understand and master their job they want to be allowed to 'handle it'.

Empowering staff in this way goes against the grain for many dentists who cry 'anarchy' at the thought of staff making their own decisions, implying that you cannot trust staff and that you need systems in order to control them. The argument goes that most people will never be passionate about their work and prefer to get paid to do a particular job in a more or less prescribed manner. If this really is the case, then why is it then that so many staff tend to be dispirited and demotivated? In most cases they know more about their job than you do so why not give them the opportunity to put into practice what they already know. They are adults after all and will, in all probability, be stricter upon themselves than you ever would be. At least give it a try. The end result is likely to be strategies that can actually be implemented.

Select the right people

In many practices hiring new staff tends to be a rather random, uncoordinated process. It shouldn't be of course and the first step is to decide what you are looking for, in other words the job design described above. When a staff opening occurs, the entire team should develop a list of criteria that the new person should possess. For example:

- A sense of belonging, a team player.
- A genuine liking for people.
- A caring attitude.
- Organisation.
- A track record of competence.
- Excellent communication skills.
- Neat appearance.

The interview needs to determine how the candidate will function in everyday job activities and so you may wish to include a member of your staff on the interview panel. Perhaps the most important thing to bear in mind is that skills can be taught, whereas personality, behaviour and attitudes are instilled. In general, the questions asked should be open-ended and allow the candidate to show their suitability to relate to other people. The following are examples of open-ended questions.

- What did you like best about your last job?

- Why did you leave your last job?
- What do you consider most important when working with patients?
- Describe how you would handle an angry or difficult patient.
- What have you done at work that you feel especially proud of?
- Why do feel you can do well in this job?

As always, listen carefully to each response and then decide on your next question. You may want the person to provide more information: 'Tell me more' or 'Can you be more specific?' Don't try and rush on to your next question. The best interviews are those where the candidate does the bulk of the talking. The more the candidate's answers match your requirements and job standards the more likely it is that that person is the one you are looking for.

Train, train and keep on training

High-quality service doesn't just happen; your staff must be trained to deliver it. In the most successful practices it always seems as though each aspect of the service delivery has been thought through and rehearsed many times. Services have been described as performances and hence the analogy with the theatre is an apt one. Everything should be choreographed and then practised so that each member of staff knows their part and knows how their role dovetails with those of the other team members. Clearly this should not be at the expense of creative problem solving as and when the need arises, but you cannot expect staff to behave as you would wish without having in place a backbone of well-planned systems. These should cover a host of activities including: telephone responses (eg if you are in private practice and a patient asks how much you charge for a crown, what would you want your receptionist to say?); new patient procedures (do you have any?); fee collection (what is your policy on fee collection and how do you minimise bad debts, recalls) and so on.

Once you have a blueprint in place for all these various activities, then you can go ahead and train your team.

In many practices staff training is at best a very *ad hoc*, poorly coordinated series of events usually handled 'on the hoof' by an experienced dental surgery assistant or front desk person who may or may not be the best person for the job. If I told you that Virgin Atlantic cabin crew were trained in this way you would rightly think I had gone mad. Why then do most practices expect top-quality service from staff without putting in place even the most basic training programme? Team training is a book in itself, but some things that need to be considered include:

- Staff who carry out the training should also be trained in how to train.
- The knowledge and skills taught match those required of the job.
- Training programmes are presented in an organised and systematic format.
- Training is divided into a series of lessons or units.
- The trainee is provided with a written copy of the training programme.
- Each skill to be taught is outlined in how-to steps.
- The standard of what constitutes an excellent job is clearly spelled out.
- The trainee is provided with a continuous flow of feedback on progress.
- A system of recording trainee progress is in place.

For a dental practice to be successful as little as possible should be allowed to happen by chance. Dental assistants can do so much more than just aspirate and receptionists can do so much more than just file records. A well-conceived training programme allows staff to reach their full potential and at the same time vastly improve the service offered to your patients.

Provide the correct rewards

Most people work for money and recognition. It is naïve to think that recognition alone is sufficient. Good staff rightly demand excellent salaries and shared bonuses. Consider the saying, 'pay peanuts and you get monkeys'. Rewards work both ways: properly rewarded staff repay through their support, loyalty and performance. Salary scales should be based on a combination of what other practices offer (market place reality), an objective assessment of what you can provide (economic reality) and your desire to pay your team well. In a good practice all three realties are given equal and fair weight.

Should you link pay to performance reviews? Opinions vary. For example, one view is that that performance reviews should be just that – an opportunity to give employees regular feedback. An excellent review may not result in an automatic pay rise, eg if the practice cannot afford it or if a raise was recently given, therefore linking the two just causes confusion and bitterness amongst staff. With this in mind, if you do decide to go ahead with performance-related

41

bonuses then they must be kept confidential.

Use modern human resource management tools

Once you have surrounded yourself with excellent people, you have to do everything in your power to keep them. One of the most striking characteristics of successful practices is a stable workforce – patients like familiar faces, and so should you. Loyalty is the result of many things: shared ideals, honesty and, as we have just said, attractive remuneration. It also comes from an awareness that you respect your staff and the jobs they do by adopting professional management techniques that are commonplace in just about every other commercial enterprise. We have already alluded to two of these techniques earlier in this chapter, namely job design and service standards. To these we must add staff meetings and providing both feedback and opportunities for growth.

Staff meetings

These should form an important part of practice life but are often dispensed with, either because staff are too busy or because the meetings have failed and caused nothing but frustration for dentists and staff. Some pointers for successful meetings are as follows.

- Schedule regular meetings, no more than 4-6 weeks apart. Extended lunchtimes enable the meeting to be split half on the staff's time and half on the dentist's time.
- Take care of business. Use meetings to ensure that people don't lose sight of the practice mission.
- Provide a safe, comfortable environment. Remember that each team member makes a valuable contribution to your practice. Shy staff should be encouraged to express their ideas. Change the seating patterns each time so that groups don't sit together. Breaking up cliques encourages discussion.
- Take turns to chair the meeting. During the month prior to the meeting, staff should bring ideas for discussion to the chairperson so they can be placed on the agenda.
- Each person should present a short report on their own area of responsibility, for example the receptionist on waiting times, cancellations and so on.
- Review the decisions made at the previous meeting.
- When dealing with topics on the agenda discuss problems but don't

degrade, embarrass or pick on others and don't mention things said in confidence. If a job has been well done give praise and appreciation.
- Make decisions. Who will be responsible for carrying out the task? How will they do it? Is there a deadline? A lack of action will soon undermine the value of the meeting.
- Set new goals. For example, increasing new patient numbers, reduce bad debts and so on.
- Have fun. Don't sulk, sigh or look bored. In fact don't use any negative body language.

Providing feedback

No one enjoys being criticised. It is an unpleasant experience that usually leaves people feeling angry, belittled and resentful. In giving staff members positive feedback the aim is to give an accurate representation of matters, which leaves the recipient with a sense of comfort so that they hear what is being said without negative feelings getting in the way. Positive feedback possesses a number of characteristics.

- Giving praise, a gift we are unwilling to give but yearn to receive. Not all feedback has to be negative – you must recognise when something has been done that warrants praise, respond straightaway and don't under-state or over-state your appreciation.
- Encouraging people. You must express your belief in the staff member's ability, in turn reinforcing their own self belief. Provide support by guidance and simply by being there. Most of all be patient.
- Concentrating on the positive. Don't mix positive feedback with negative feedback: the person will only hear the negative.
- Avoid being patronising. By concentrating on the work and the staff member's performance rather than making personal judgements about the person it is possible to be clear and direct without the risk of being condescending.

In his book *Motivating People to Perform,* Trevor Bentley (1996) suggests the following four-step approach.

State what happens – 'When you do…'
State how you feel – 'I feel…'

43

State why – 'Because…'
State what you want – 'I would prefer it if you…'

This form of communication is very powerful because it is open and honest and yet is entirely positive in nature.

Opportunities for growth

Many of the problems dentists face in motivating their staff spring from a perceived lack of professional development. Whatever the job, most people need to feel it is leading somewhere. An excellent way to stimulate staff members is to encourage them to participate in development programmes, and to convey to them that you back their efforts. Supporting your staff's attendance on continuing education courses and providing them with books, videos and other materials begins this growth process. If anyone decides to explore other jobs in the dental field, don't discourage them. In fact you should actively encourage them. You will either end up with dissatisfied employees who stay in the practice, or lose out on rehiring those individuals who would otherwise take their upgraded skills elsewhere.

Quality leadership

Much has been written on the subject of leadership, all of which applies just as much to a dentist running a dental practice as it does to those guiding multinational corporations. It is widely held that good leaders:

- Are excellent communicators. Good leaders communicate their thoughts clearly and with enthusiasm. They also are very good listeners.
- Use their power wisely. Power is never used just because it is there but is used as a means of maintaining standards which in turn allow the realisation of the practice mission and goals. This can only happen when excellence in communication and rewards are established and in place.
- Are good decision makers. This trait is synonymous with good leaders. Making right decisions in turn increases staff support for their leader, especially when others are allowed to participate in the decision-making process. Even so, many decisions will result in unhappiness or resentment somewhere in the practice. This should not prevent that decision being made if it is the right one. As Lady Thatcher once said, 'Never flinch –

make up your mind and do it'. At the end of the day you are the boss.
• Create an energy that compels other to follow. This relates back to what George Bush called 'this vision thing'. Good leaders create an ambience of vitality, a positive working environment, an infectious optimism – all abstract forces that are difficult to define but you know right away when they are not there. This positive energy is what results in a mission being translated into a reality and in so doing helps give others guidance and direction.

None of these characteristics mean anything however if they are not accompanied by solid management expertise. Particularly in relatively small enterprises such as a dental practice, you cannot be successful as a leader without also being an effective manager. Winning teams don't just happen, they are carefully planned and nourished by providing continuous attention. If any confirmation were needed of this simple truth read the words of an experienced DSA, Sally Chadwick.

Carry on nurse!

I recently met a girl I used to go to school with. I have only seen her a few times since we left, 18 years ago. She was amazed to hear that I was still working with the same dentist in the same practice that I joined as soon as I left school.

The early days of being a dental nurse can be tedious if you are only assigned to changing x-ray developer chemicals and making the tea. But I have found that, with a good training programme and regular reviews, dental nurses can and do stay interested and motivated and enjoy a long, rewarding career. Simple, informal chats in which staff members define their roles within the practice and discuss their future goals, for example to further their dental careers by training to become a hygienist, will help to structure nurses' development. With good communication everybody should be happy.

What a shame so many dental nurses leave so early in their dental careers. Speaking to some, I found it was a combination of poor pay, long hours and most of all, a lack of appreciation that had left them dissatisfied. A friend I had qualified with left her job as a dental nurse after two years because she was fed up of working with somebody who constantly took her for granted and who was of the opinion that dental nurses should be seen and not heard. (I wouldn't have lasted two days let alone two years!)

45

Working long hours is sometimes necessary and a simple 'thank you for your help' can make all the difference. The fact that you had worked all your lunch hours for a week will suddenly seem less important, because you know it was appreciated. Then maybe, instead of ringing in sick the next week, dental nurses will come back smiling. After all without a dental nurse, a dentist's work is infinitely harder and more stressful.

Teamwork brings satisfaction all round. Working as a partnership is essential and from my experience working with the same dentist for so many years means that I am very familiar with the way he works and, because we always discuss treatment plans, I know what we are trying to achieve.

Knowing why a patient requires a certain treatment and being able to see what is happening in the mouth are fundamental to increasing a nurse's experience. Simply being shown the inside of the patient's mouth (for example, using an intra-oral camera) will keep nurses involved and better informed about dental procedures.

Just look at all the dynamic duos there have been, Batman and Robin, the Lone Ranger and Tonto. It goes to show that working in pairs does seem to be better (although my partner in my chemistry lessons may disagree!). Most super heroes have a trusty sidekick and while I'm sure not all dentists wear masks, capes and long boots (at least not at work), having somebody to discuss things with can be very helpful.

To ensure that patients are greeted by friendly, familiar staff and not a new face every six months, dentists need to show more appreciation and encourage further training to help expand the jobs of their dental nurses into ones that are interesting and rewarding. Everybody wins then.

Sally Chadwick

Summary

- Patient satisfaction is closely tied to employee satisfaction.
- A well-organised, motivated team is an essential prerequisite for dental practice success.
- A number of steps must be followed in order to create such a team: service standards; staff selection; training programmes; reward systems; staff meetings; provision of feedback to staff.
- Dentists must demonstrate leadership characteristics if they are to build a winning team.

Gathering and using feedback

5

Measure what is measurable and make measurable what is not.

Galileo Galilei, astronomer

It should be clear by now that the extent to which your patients are satisfied with the service you provide plays a pivotal role in shaping the success of your practice. There are a number of other important reasons to try and measure patient satisfaction.

• Ratings of consumer satisfaction enable management to determine the need for, as well as the effectiveness of, changes aimed at reducing any gaps between what patients want and expect, and what they perceive they have received.
• Ratings of satisfaction are useful for enhancing staff training programmes.
• Ratings may help gain insight about competitors.
• If favourable, it may be possible and appropriate to include ratings in promotional materials.

But what is the best way to go about measuring patient satisfaction in dental practice? While it is possible to measure satisfaction unobtrusively and indirectly by collecting data on its effects (eg profits, patient complaints and retention number, etc) far more useful information can be gathered by measuring it directly. Certainly the most common approach is to conduct a questionnaire survey of some of the practice's patients. Such surveys:

• Are relatively cheap.
• Are easy to carry out.
• Provide formal feedback in a quantitative form that allows for the monitoring of performance.
• Are highly visible and send out positive signals not only to patients but also to staff members, that concern for patient opinion is being taken seriously.

A considerable number of studies have been written up in the dental literature over the past thirty years or so. These studies usually focus on patient perceptions of the dental provider and tend to ignore other important antecedent factors, such as expectations and desires. Commonly, the perceptions assessed comprise some or all of the seven Cs discussed in Chapter 3, namely cues, comfort, convenience, care, communication, courtesy and cost. Published studies of dental patient satisfaction nearly always reveal very high levels of satisfaction, with a majority of patients surveyed seemingly satisfied with their dentist. Not only that but the modal response, ie the value that occurs most frequently, is typically the most positive response allowed by the questionnaire.

There are two possible explanations for such a distinctive pattern of distribution. The first is that it reflects actual satisfaction, ie patients are for the most part satisfied with the services offered by their dentist. What rational consumer would knowingly purchase a service that is not expected to satisfy some want or need? Alternatively, it may be that the findings are misleading and, for whatever reason, do not reflect 'true' satisfaction. Put simply, such questionnaires might not actually measure what they are supposed to measure. Most questionnaires tend to collapse diverse opinions into a single category of users, all of who express 'satisfaction'. Consider the following statements.

- 'I've evaluated the service offered and I'm happy with it.'
- 'I don't really think I have the ability to evaluate, but I do have confidence in the staff.'
- 'The service offered was appalling but I don't like to criticise, after all they're doing their best.'

Increasingly, concerns are being raised over the methodological validity of satisfaction questionnaires, leading one researcher to observe that:

> *Questionnaires can act as a form of censorship imposed on patients. They give misleading results, limit the opportunity of patients to express their concerns about different aspects of care, and can encourage professionals to believe that patients are satisfied when in reality they are highly discontented.*
> Whitfield, M, Baker, R.

While all this certainly does not make such surveys redundant, it has to be accepted that many questionnaires are unnecessarily blunt. Clearly, great care has to be exercised in their composition and implementation to ensure that

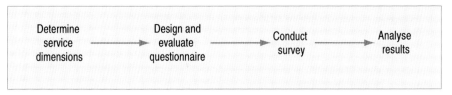

Fig. 5.1 A general model for the development and use of customer satisfaction questionnaires.

they are valid and reflect reality. Questionnaires have to be designed in such a way as to embody the way patients truly feel about dentists, employing terms that patients would, and do, use to express those feelings. A general model for the development and use of satisfaction questionnaires is shown in Figure 5.1.

Step one in the process is to identify those aspects or dimensions of the service that are considered important by the consumers of that service, ie patients. The seven Cs are a good starting point, as are the various dimensions of care used by the many surveys of dental patient satisfaction that have appeared in the dental literature. One of the best known is the self-administered 19-item Dental Satisfaction Questionnaire described by Davies and Ware (1981). Sources of this type, however, should be seen only as a starting point. The drawback of relying solely on such 'off the shelf' questions and item statements is that they are unlikely to be tailored to the specific situation a practice finds itself in and so may yield results devoid of much real meaning.

Qualitative research

One way of creating a meaningful questionnaire is to carry out preliminary qualitative research aimed at identifying patient requirements more fully and in terms that patients use. Qualitative research comprises an array of techniques that help us gain deeper insights into people and situations. These techniques help us come to terms with 'meaning' rather than 'frequency' and are an excellent source of information on patient views in their own right. They also serve to generate ideas for later incorporation into a questionnaire survey. Many different types of technique fall under the umbrella of qualitative research. One is the 'critical incident' technique that is being used increasingly in conjunction with focus group interviews to find out more about how products and services are perceived by consumers. The strength of the 'critical incident' technique lies in its use of an organisation's own customers to define good service. Once again it is worth stressing the point that reliance on standards generated without reference to a practice's own patients is likely to lead to an inappropriate battery of questions.

A 'critical incident' describes either positive or negative performance by the service provider. Thus, a positive example is a characteristic of the service provided by the practice that the patient would like to see repeated every time. A negative example is a characteristic of the service that would make the patient question the quality of the practice. The procedure involves two steps. In the first, patients are interviewed to obtain specific information about the service. In the second, this information is categorised into groups, each group reflecting a dimension of service. The interviews can be done either in person or over the telephone, individually or in groups, and it is usually recommended to interview at least ten people to ensure sufficient material is generated. Group interviews have the advantage that critical incidents stated by one person may stimulate comments from other group members. For example, the interviewer should ask each person to describe five positive and five negative instances of the service they have received in the past. Patients may feel reluctant to 'open up' and for group interviews it makes sense to choose a location away from the practice and with someone unrelated to the practice acting as group mediator. While all this clearly complicates the whole process of data collection, the benefits in terms of the quality of feedback received are enormous. If, during the interview, a patient uses general terms such as 'the dentist was nice', the interviewer should determine what it was, in behavioural terms, that made the dentist 'nice'. By pressing the interviewees to supply specific examples of performance or specific adjectives to describe the service, the interviewer will in turn obtain specific critical incidents, which will greatly enhance the final questionnaire.

This process will generate a long list of critical incidents. Similar incidents that focus on a specific aspect of the service should be grouped together. Once these clusters have been formed it is possible to write a phrase for each one that reflects the content of its incidents. This phrase is called a satisfaction item. For example, the following three critical incidents, each from different people, would fall under one satisfaction item.

- 'I waited too long before I was seen.'
- 'I was in a big hurry but had to wait in line for a very long time.'
- 'I only had to wait for a very short time.'

A satisfaction item that would encompass these three incidents could be:

• 'I waited a short period of time before I was seen by the dentist.'

The respondent will be asked in the questionnaire to agree or disagree with this statement. It can be seen that both positive and negative critical incidents can be included under one satisfaction item. The three incidents listed above, even though they reflect positive and negative aspects of service are all reflected in the word 'wait'. Therefore, the satisfaction item is written to include the word 'wait'. Related items can be grouped under a heading labelled 'responsiveness of service'. For example:

• 'I was kept informed if the dentist was running late.'

These satisfaction items are used as building blocks in step two of the development model; questionnaire design. A few well-accepted principles should be followed when putting together self-completed questionnaires.

Questionnaire design

Use specific questions and statements
In responding to the question, 'How satisfied are you with the availability of the services we offer?', different people will have different definitions of the word 'availability'. Better to ask patients to respond to more specific statements that leave less room for varying interpretations, for example, 'I could get an appointment at a time I wanted' or, 'My appointment was at a convenient time'

Open-ended versus closed questions
Closed questions that ask the respondent to choose from specific, predefined answers are the most commonly used and are generally easier to analyse. However, open-ended questions are often useful in that they allow the respondents to express themselves more fully, especially if no preliminary qualitative research has been carried out. For example, the question, 'Did anything happen during your visit that surprised you? If so please tell us what it was', should be followed only by the following prompts, 'Good Surprise' and 'Bad surprise' and a space to write a description.

51

Ask for relative rather than absolute evaluations

Try asking patients how particular aspects of the service compared to something or someone else, eg 'Was the dentist more or less friendly than your GP?' This gives patients a standard from which to evaluate and tends to lead to more accurate representation of their views. People rarely evaluate in absolute terms.

Be concise

Keep questions and statements short and to the point otherwise the questionnaire can become too long and difficult to read. Use everyday language and simple words rather than complex ones. For example replace, 'The receptionist seemed to act in a very pleasant manner whenever I had to deal with her' with, 'The receptionist was very pleasant'.

Once the items and statements have been formulated, the next step is to choose a response format. This determines how patients can respond to the items on the questionnaire.

Response formats

Checklist format

This works on the principle that the quality of a service can be quantified by the number of positive things said about it and so for each item in the questionnaire respondents can answer 'yes' or 'no'. The benefit of this method is the ease with which the questionnaire can be completed. The disadvantage is the lack of variability of scores that result from the scale. This can be overcome by using a scaled response format such as the Likert scale or the Semantic Differential.

Likert format

This allows responses of varying degrees to a list of statements that describe the service or product.

Example 1

Please indicate the extent to which you agree or disagree with the following statements about the service you receive from our practice. Please circle the appropriate number.

My appointment started promptly at the scheduled time	Strongly disagree	Somewhat disagree	No opinion	Somewhat agree	Strongly agree
	1	2	3	4	5

Given the importance of expectations and desires in formulating satisfaction it is particularly important to try and measure their strength. The following example is useful in determining whether a particular aspect of the service was better or worse than that anticipated or hoped for.

Example 2

Please indicate a) how important the following are to you and b) how satisfied you are with our performance in each area. Please circle the appropriate number.

	Importance	Satisfaction
I like to know beforehand how much my treatment is going to cost	1 2 3 4 5	1 2 3 4 5
	1 = not all important 5 = extremely important	1 = not all satisfied 5 = extremely satisfied

Semantic Differential

In this technique respondents are invited to place a concept or idea on a seven-point scale anchored by a pair of adjectives. For example:

'How would you describe our practice?'
Please place an X at the position on each scale that reflects your opinion.

Friendly |___|___|___|___|___|___| Unfriendly

By using a range of adjectives the semantic differential can be used to develop a profile of the patients' view of the service offered.

After its design has been finalised, the questionnaire should be pretested in a small pilot study to ensure that the questions and statements can be understood and that the way to record responses is clearly explained. The questionnaire should flow naturally, maintaining the respondent's interest. Once a respondent is committed to the questionnaire they will usually stick it out to the end but if you have lost their interest, it is quite likely that they will take the path of least resistance, at best going for the middle ground and at worst giving false answers, in an effort to get through the exercise.It is also important that patients are able to complete the questionnaire anonymously and with this in mind it is probably better to include a prepaid envelope with the questionnaire.

This section only presents an overview of the steps involved in conducting a satisfaction survey. While there are a number of excellent guides available (eg Morgan and Spanish [1985]; Fink [1995]; Goften and Ness [1997]) the best way to learn about the survey process is simply to go out and have a go.

Using the information gathered

Gathering information is only useful if it is then used in a meaningful way to drive service improvement and, consequently, patient satisfaction. The methods just described are of most use in flagging up those areas where service delivery is seen by patients to be failing. These techniques also tend to produce large amounts of information, which must then be presented in a way that is easily understood by everyone in the practice. Only by sharing the results of the research does it become possible to implement changes that will lead to improved service. Staff members are, after all, the ones who will be expected to put into action many of the initiatives borne of this whole process.

A number of management tools have been devised to help organise this information in such a way that allows us to move away from asking 'what' to asking 'why'.

Why–why analysis

This is a simple but effective technique for helping to understand what is causing a problem. It starts by describing the problem and asking why it has arisen. Once the major reasons have been identified, each one is taken in turn, and again the question is asked why those factors have occurred. This procedure is continued until either a cause seems obvious enough to be addressed by itself or no more answers to the question 'why?' can be generated.

Cause–effect diagrams

Also known as fishbone or Ishikawa diagrams these build upon the 'why–why?' approach and are very effective in helping find the root causes of problems. The technique is used extensively in quality improvement programmes and is particularly helpful as a guide for group discussions, keeping meetings on target and educating staff members in the process of problem solving. There are four steps involved in using a cause–effect diagram.

Step one
Write down the problem being analysed.

Step two
Identify the main categories of possible causes of the problem.

Step three
Ask questions to identify possible causes under these categories. For example:
- What activities are carried out and why?
- How are things done and why?
- When are things done and why?
- Who carries out the activities and why?
- How many times do things happen and why?

Step four
Record all potential causes on the diagram under each category and discuss each item to combine and clarify the causes.

The general form of the cause–effect diagram is shown in Figure 5.2.

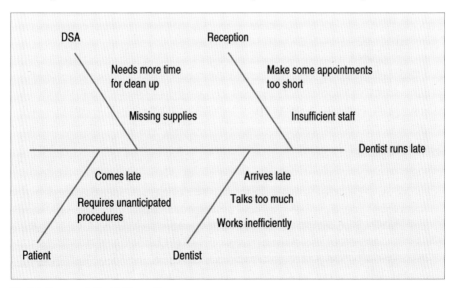

Fig. 5.2 Cause and effect fishbone diagram.

In the example shown, the problem under review is that one of the dentists in a group practice is experiencing problems running on time. Using a flip chart, staff members list all the possible causes of an appointment running late. The different causes are organised into categories, with specific issues under each category. This process allows staff to appreciate how other activities in the practice cause appointments to run late, and in particular it highlights the interdependence of staff on each other. To get the most out of cause–effect diagrams try and follow these simple guidelines:

- Use separate diagrams for each problem.
- Make sure diagrams are visible to everyone involved.
- Don't overload diagrams – use separate diagrams for each major category if necessary.
- Be prepared to rework and refine categories.
- Don't use vague statements such as 'possible lack of' – always be specific.
- Circle causes that seem particularly significant.

Importance/performance matrix

This is one of the most useful forms of analysis. It combines, on the one hand, information about expectations with, on the other, ratings of the actual service provided. An example is shown in Figure 5.3 with importance represented on the vertical axis from high (top) to low (bottom).

Performance is shown on the horizontal axis from low (left) to high (right). The box situated at the top left-hand corner contains those features most in need of improvement – their importance to patients is high and yet perceived performance is low. These are the areas the practice must put its energies into improving.

Summary

- Most questionnaire surveys reveal very high levels of patient satisfaction.
- Qualitative research techniques such as the 'critical incident' technique and focus groups give deeper insight into your patients' views, and can be used to design more realistic, grounded questionnaires.
- Collecting feedback from patients is only worthwhile if the information is then used to improve service. A number of techniques assist in this, such as why–why analysis, cause–effect diagrams and the importance/performance matrix.

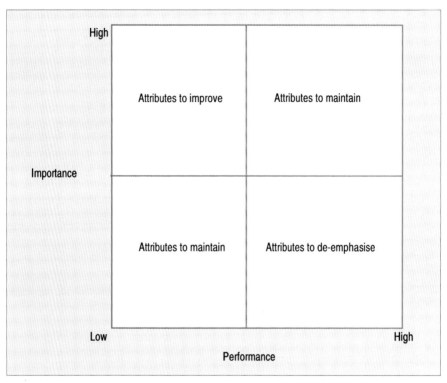

Fig. 5.3 The importance/performance matrix.

Patient dissatisfaction – what it is and how to deal with it when it happens

6

You ponce in here expecting to be waited on hand and foot, well I'm trying to run a hotel here. Have you any idea how much there is to do? Do you ever think of that? Of course not, you're all too busy sticking your noses into every corner, poking around for things to complain about, aren't you?

Basil Fawlty, fictional hotelier

Dissatisfaction? Surely the opposite of satisfaction…or is it? In his definitive text on attitude measurement, Oppenheim (1997) noted that we tend to see behavioural phenomena, such as satisfaction, as running in straight lines, from positive, through neutral, to negative. There is, however, no conclusive proof that this linear continuum is a true representation although, as we shall see in this chapter, it certainly does make things easier for measurement purposes. With tongue firmly in cheek, Oppenheim suggested that for all we know these attitudes may be shaped more like concentric circles, overlapping ellipses or even three-dimensional cloud formations. Conventional wisdom perpetuates this idea of a continuum, holding that 'bad' experiences will automatically translate into dissatisfaction and that the worse the encounter the greater the extent of the dissatisfaction. Intuitively this seems perfectly logical – if someone has had a bad experience at the dentist they cannot possibly be satisfied and therefore by definition they must be dissatisfied. This approach, however, fails to take into account the process of 'naming, blaming and claiming' in which expressions of dissatisfaction only tend to arise when the patient feels that the dentist or staff are to blame for the service failure that led to the bad experience. The flow chart shown in Figure 6.1 indicates possible thought processes patients might go through. To show how this works, let us suppose that the experience in question relates to the booking of a dental appointment. The first question the patient asks is, 'Did the dentist behave in the way I think a dentist should behave? That is, did they match my perception of their duty?' If the patient had made the appointment for a certain time but that morning the practice phoned to say that an earlier time slot had become available, which was more convenient for the

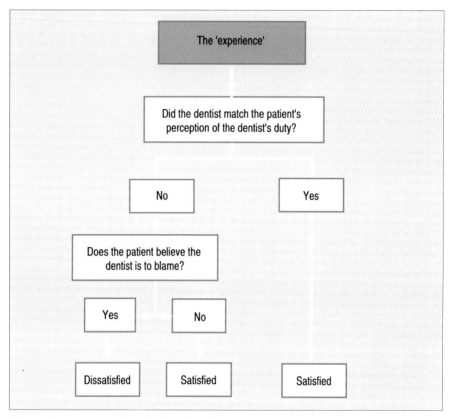

Fig. 6.1 The consequences of good and bad experiences.

patient, then the patient would probably feel that practice staff had gone above and beyond their duty. The patient would therefore be likely to say that they were 'very satisfied' with that aspect of care. Alternatively, if the appointment went ahead at the arranged time, with no delay, then the patient would tend to feel that practice staff had carried out their duty – no more, no less – and therefore would likely be 'satisfied'. So far, so good. What I have just described is very much in line with the disconfirmation of expectations theory discussed in Chapter 3. Imagine though that the patient turned up at the allotted time, but had to wait for forty-five minutes before being seen. The patient will ask the question, 'Were the dentist and their staff to blame for this?' The answer might actually be 'No'. What if, for example, at the same time as the patient's appointment a young boy is brought in following an accident. The child is clearly distressed and in considerable pain, there are broken teeth and torn soft tissues. The dentist explains in person to the first patient that he really must attend to the emergency immediately, apologises for the inconvenience, offers to reschedule the appointment and so on. In this situation the 'wronged' patient is still likely to express satisfaction despite not receiving the service hoped for or expected. Put simply, the patient sees that this behaviour is caring and professional and believes that the dentist cannot be blamed for the situation that has arisen. The patient may even be extremely satisfied for choosing to visit such a kind considerate dentist! Alternatively, the circumstances may be very different – the dentist is running late, no explanation has been offered, no apology made and no attempt made to rectify the situation. In this case the answer to the question may well be, 'Yes, I think the dentist is to blame.' It is only now that the patient is likely to express dissatisfaction

It does appear then that it takes quite a lot to make patients dissatisfied – at least to the extent that they see you and your practice as the sole cause of their dissatisfaction. Unfortunately, once a patient begins to feel dissatisfied in this way, they not only become aware of service quality but also become increasingly 'sensitised' to it. As the patient begins to drop further and further beyond the lower limits of their particular 'zone of tolerance' they start to look for other problems to support their feelings of dissatisfaction. Accordingly, the perceived levels of care of other aspects of the service delivery that the patient, under normal circumstances, would find acceptable, now begin to become unacceptable. This explains the finding that service performance that falls below expectations tends to be rated poorer than it is in reality. The converse is also true, ie service performance above expectations tends to be rated very highly. In other words, consumers are thought to magnify ratings in the direction of the disconfirmation. We have all seen examples of this. Patients often refer to previous dentists in extreme terms, either 'Butcher' and 'Attila the Hun' or 'Saint' and 'The Queen doesn't get better treatment' and so on.

Consequences of dissatisfaction

When patients are unhappy with the service they have received, they can do several things, all of which are bad news when you are trying to build your practice upon a foundation of trusting, long-term relationships. These actions can involve either 'exit' (leaving the practice and never coming back) or 'voice' (telling someone about their bad experience) or a combination of the two. Before we get too depressed though about all this, let us be realistic. There is no such thing as the perfect dental practice in which everything happens exactly as it should, where staff behave in the same perfect way day in, day out and where patients are totally satisfied with every aspect of the service received. As Christopher Hart (1990), writing in the *Harvard Business Review*, observed:

> *Mistakes are a critical part of every service…errors are inevitable. But dissatisfied customers are not. While companies may not be able to prevent all problems, they can learn to recover from them. A good recovery can turn angry, frustrated customers into loyal ones.*

You can't please all the people all the time; the secret lies in knowing how to deal with dissatisfied patients. The first step is to identify them before they start wrecking your image and that of your practice. A good percentage of such patients will be obvious to you. Situations such as people being kept waiting, people whose appointments you have had to cancel at the last moment, obvious clinical mistakes and so on. Be pro-active in these situations. Don't just sit back and wait for bad things to happen. In a number of other cases you may simply be unaware of the dissatisfaction felt until the patient complains to you. By paying attention to complaints, patient loyalty improves dramatically. Many would even argue that the key to a successful business is to encourage customers to complain. This view is borne out by one US National Consumer Survey which found that 54% of shoppers dissatisfied with services or products worth more than US$100 would buy again if the complaint were resolved satisfactorily. This figure dropped to 19% when the complaint was not resolved to the consumer's satisfaction. Significantly, when a complaint was not made despite dissatisfaction, only 9% of consumers would buy again. The message, albeit daunting, is clear – service providers, including dentists, must actively solicit complaints. Large companies invest millions to improve complaint handling. They see complaints as a vital source of consumer feedback. While the scale may be different, dental practices can approach the problem in a similar manner with damage-control techniques aimed at converting critics into loyal supporters. This certainly applies to the administrative problems of dental practice, such as errors in billing patients, double-booking and undelivered laboratory work. As was discussed in Chapter 3, most of the dissatisfaction arising from problems following treatment, eg postoperative pain and swelling, can be minimised by careful explanation and modification of patient expectations to reflect reality more closely.

What would you do if you, as the practice principal, received this letter?

Dear Sir

I am writing to express my dissatisfaction and disappointment at the way your associate Dr G handled my case. I came to your practice earlier this year in January and over the next three months was given a bridge and four veneers. During this time I was not treated in a professional manner. On a number of occasions I was called late in the afternoon to be informed that my appointment for the following day had been cancelled. As a result I continually had to keep rearranging my own schedule. Even after I raised my concerns to Dr G and to the receptionist there was no improvement. Dr G never treated me with courtesy or consideration and never tried to explain what he was doing or why he was doing it. His attitude was always 'take it or leave it'.

As for the treatment the colour of the finished veneers didn't match the colour of my own teeth. He also left a crack in one of them. The false tooth is longer than my original tooth. If it wasn't for the nice nurse he wouldn't have been able to finish my teeth at all. All I have to say is that he has put me through a lot of pain and frustration and the final result is unsatisfactory.

A very unhappy patient.

Ms D

Dealing with dissatisfaction

Creating the opportunity to complain

The effects of failure to return and negative word of mouth are so damaging that you have to do all you can to create the opportunity for aggrieved patients to voice their dissatisfaction to you. That is before they quit your practice and before they start spreading their bad news to other patients and potential patients. This allows recovery to take place. Unfortunately, many dentists seem to go to great lengths to suppress complaints, thus losing valuable information as well as existing and future clients. Dentists should encourage the use of anonymous suggestion forms, which ask the simple question, 'What could we do to improve our care for you?' Giving your patients the opportunity to help flatters them and also elicits many small complaints that patients had intended to let pass. Taking a worst case scenario, the more avenues and opportunities a patient has to complain the less likely it is that any complaint will lead to litigation. Figures from Dental Protection Ltd provide ample illustration of this point. In New Zealand, there are nine other complaint pathways, which are much quicker, cheaper and more effective for the patient than wrestling with civil litigation. While in the Republic of Ireland, on the other hand, the patient has nowhere to go except the Dental Council or to a solicitor in order to pursue a civil action. The result is that malpractice claims account for less than 5% of the company's work in New Zealand against a staggering 80% in Ireland.

Recovery procedures
It is important to recognise that all customers have recovery expectations that they want service providers to meet. It follows that recovery needs to be a planned process that will meet the needs and expectations of dissatisfied patients. If a problem arises and the practice does not have set recovery procedures in place, staff will be forced to make instant decisions that could make the problem worse. Procedures should already be in place to deal with difficult patients who come ready for battle.

Timing
When dealing with problems try and select a time when you are able to be a good listener. Of course this isn't easy but it is best to avoid times when you are tired and preoccupied. Problem solving is not easy when you have to simultaneously deal with other issues and responsibilities.

Acknowledgement
Acknowledge the complaint and accept that the problem exists. Resist the temptation to look on patients as irritating nuisances.

Apology
You should recognise that the patient is a victim of the service breakdown. Apologise immediately, otherwise patients may assume that what they are compaining about is normal in the practice. It is wise for the dentist to make the apology even if they were not directly involved. Patients find it difficult to express their irritation to someone who is, in their eyes, innocent.

Empathy
See the situation from the patient's point of view. This demonstrates

compassion and understanding for the injured party. By saying, 'I know how you feel' you are showing concern for the patient, not just the problem. When service fails, first treat the person and then fix the problem.

Action

Swift action is vital, not only to show that the situation is being dealt with but also to prevent dissemination of the bad news. Problems with service delivery often escalate swiftly, so a top priority must be to complete the service as quickly as possible.

Atonement

Restoration of normal service coupled with an apology will placate most patients. But some situations may demand a more symbolic gesture of atonement. Service recovery does not just mean a return to a normal state but a state of enhanced perception. All breakdowns require you to jump through a few hoops to get the patient back to neutral. More hoops are required for victims to recover. Depending on the nature of the particular patient you might, for example, consider sending a book or record token along with the letter of apology. At the very least, you should consider writing to the patient to thank them for their complaint.

Follow-up

Where the complaint leads to the implementation of corrective measures, the patient should be told. This demonstrates an appreciation of the value of the criticism and continuing care and concern. If the problem cannot be solved, then a simple explanation should be given as to why.

With consumers smarter and more discerning than ever, paying attention to, even courting, complainers has become an essential part of modern business. That it can also be good business is an added bonus.

Summary

- Not all negative incidents will result in patient dissatisfaction.
- Patient complaints should be encouraged.
- When patients do complain, recovery procedures should already be established and in place.

References

Bader J, Sams D. Office personnel differ in assessing management strategies. *J Am Dent Assoc* 1992; 123: 119-127.

Bee F, Bee R. *Customer Care.* London: Institute of Personnel Development 1995.

Bentley T. Sharpen your skills in motivating people to perform. London: McGraw-Hill, 1996.

Davies A, Ware J. Measuring patient satisfaction with dental care. *Social Science and Medicine* 1981; 15: 751-760.

Fink A. *The Survey Kit.* London: Sage, 1995.

Goften L, Ness M. *Business Market Research.* London, Kogan Page, 1997.

Hamric R. Common traits of the million-dollar practice. *Dental Economics* 1996 June; 35-47.

Harrison R. How to describe your organisation. *Harvard Business Review* 1972, Sept/Oct

Hart C. The profitable art of service recovery. *Harvard Business Review* 1990 July/August; 148-155.

Janal D. *Marketing on the Internet.* New York, John Wiley, 2000.

Johns T. *Perfect Customer Care.* London, Arrow Books 1994.

Kellaway L. *Sense and nonsense in the office,* London, Practice Hall 2000

Levitt T. Marketing myopia. *Harvard Business Review* 1960 July/August; 45-56.

Martin W B. *Managing Quality Customer Service.* London, Kogan Page 1989.

Martin W B. *Quality Customer Service for Front Line Staff.* London, Kogan Page, 1993.

Morgan D, Spanish M. Social interaction and the cognitive organisation of health-relevant behavior. *Sociology of Health and Illness* 1985; 7: 410-422.

Oppenheim A. *Questionnaire Design, Interviewing and Attitude Measurement.* London, Pinter Publishers Ltd, 1997.

Peters T, Waterman R. *In Search of Excellence: Lessons form America's Best Run Companies.* New York, Harper and Row, 1982.

Whitfield M, Baker R. Measuring patient satisfaction for audit in general practice. Quality Health Care 1992; 3: 151.

Index